A COTSWOLD BOOK

What, and where, are these creatures?

Margaret Caine and Alan Gorton

S. B. Publications

By the same authors
Curiosities of Gloucestershire – The Cotswolds
Curiosities of Gloucestershire – The Severn Valley and Forest of Dean
Cotswold Follies and Fancies
Curiosities of Warwickshire

To the Committee of Ladies,
Chris, Janet, Lesley and Vicky,
who never cease to explore, inquire and wonder.

First published in 2000 by S. B. Publications,
19 Grove Road, Seaford, East Sussex BN25 1TP

ISBN 1 85770 212 3

Designed and typeset by CGB, Lewes
Printed by MFP Design and Print
Longford Trading Estate, Thomas Street,
Stretford, Manchester M32 0JT

CONTENTS

Front cover: Name this Indian-style house near Moreton-in-Marsh.
Back cover: What is this creature – and what church does it adorn?

INTRODUCTION

It could be argued that a quiz book needs no introduction; it is quite a simple idea and we are familiar with quizzes of every kind as they assail us from all sections of the media. Similarly, the subject of this one, the Cotswolds, is so well known that they too need no further introduction. But is this so?

We are all fascinated by testing our knowledge against those we consider to have a little more expertise than ourselves, to try to outscore them, and even to outwit them. In this book we have created questions that are straightforward, none are cryptic, none are meant to mislead. They range from the relatively easy to the very difficult.

We have selected carefully from the range of historical, geographical, agricultural, industrial, military, political and religious possibilities and added questions on myth and legend. The questions will certainly test your knowledge of the Cotswolds, and will, hopefully, encourage you to search deeper into those topics or areas where your knowledge has been found wanting.

Margaret Caine and Alan Gorton
Shipston on Stour
Summer 2000

1 COUNTY RECORDS

*. . . the most English and least spoilt of
all our countrysides.*

J B Priestley of the Cotswolds in
English Journey, 1933.

1 Which is the tallest tower on the Cotswolds?

2 From the top of which tower can be seen the most counties in England?

3 Where is the tallest yew hedge in Gloucestershire?

4 Name the biggest country house in the Cotswolds?

5 Which village pub's name is unique?

6 Name the highest town in the Cotswolds?

7 Where is the highest point on the Cotswold escarpment?

8 And how high is it?

9 Where is the biggest clock in Gloucestershire?

10 Where is the oldest pottery in Gloucestershire?

2 ALL ABOUT ANIMALS

There is sorrow enough in the natural way
From men and women to fill our day;
But when we are certain of sorrow in store,
Why do we always arrange for more?
Brothers and Sisters, I bid you beware
Of giving your heart for a dog to tear.

Rudyard Kipling (1865-1936).
The Power of the Dog.

1 For which type of farming are the 'clear waters of the river Coln' used at Bibury?
2 Why has Cheltenham put pigeons on its coat of arms?
3 What kind of cattle are kept at Broadway Tower Country Park?
4 At Chastleton House, near Chipping Norton, cows and pigeons are housed together. How?
5 On the market house at Minchinhampton 'cubs' are mentioned on a list of tolls. What were 'cubs' and how much did they cost?
6 Who was the creator of Birdland at Bourton-on-the-Water?
7 And to conserve what creatures did he buy two of the Falkland Islands?
8 What was *'outrun on Cotsall'*?
9 What was the name of the dog buried in the dogs' cemetery at Stanway House and which describes a particular olfactory reaction to him?
10 Where is Wag the horse buried?

3 BIRDS – AND SOME BEASTS

There was an Old Man with a beard,
Who said, 'It is just as I feared! –
Two owls and a hen,
Four larks and a wren,
Have all built their nests in my beard!'

Edward Lear (1812-1888) *Book of Nonsense*

1 Who is Flight Lieutenant Frederick and where can he be seen?

2 What fair takes place twice a year at Stow-on-the-Wold?

3 Where can you adopt a pig for £15, an owl for £30 and a camel for £50?

4 Where is the headquarters of the Barn Owl Conservation Trust?

5 Where is the largest dovecote in Gloucestershire?

6 What is a potence?

7 The church of St John, Elkstone, is the only one on the Cotswolds with a columbarium above the chancel. What is this?

8 What is the name given to unfledged pigeons?

9 Kenley Lass from Cirencester won the Dicken Medal for conspicuous bravery in Occupied France during the Second World War. What was she?

10 On which 800 acre reserve are there up to 8,000 wild winter birds?

4 CRIME AND PUNISHMENT

Prison is an effective deterrent to those who walk past the gate, not through it.

Roger Attrill, Governor of Winson Green Prison, Birmingham, in the *New Statesman*, September 1980.

1 Name two of the four Cotswold towns/villages which have retained (unused) their lockups.

2 What is known locally as 'The Dumpling House' in Cirencester?

3 How many footholes are there in the stocks at Winchcombe?

4 Where were spectacles used as punishment?

5 What was the 'Campden Wonder'?

6 Name the two brothers who were hanged at Gloucester and their bodies brought back to the scene of their crimes,to be gibbetted and left to rot in chains on the Gibbet Oak beside the Fulbrook to Shipton-under-Wychwood road a little north of Capp's Lodge.

7 Who was involved in the 'unnatural murther' of Sir Thomas Overbury of Bourton-on-the-Hill in London in 1615?

8 On the Fosse Way near Northleach is one of four prisons established about 1790. By which Cotswold social reformer?

9 Name one of the other three prisons built for the county on the same plan.

10 What subsequent miscarriage of justice resulted from the discovery by two poachers of a wounded gamekeeper under a tree at Swinbrook, which became known as Millins Oak?

5 SPORTS AND PASTIMES

1 What do the contestants chase down Cooper's Hill, Brockworth on the annual Spring Bank Holiday?

2 Mrs Jan Byles and her son, Daniel, rowed a boat across the Atlantic Ocean in 1998. Which Cotswold town did they live in?

3 Gone are the balmy days of Bibury Races, but Bibury Race Club, the oldest racing club in Britain established in 1681, is still very much in being and since 1899 has operated all the races at which course?

4 Cheltenham Races have never actually been held in Cheltenham. Where are they held?

5 The first classic race of the National Hunt season is run here in November. What is it called?

6 And what is the major race of the day before the Gold Cup is run?

7 Badminton is synonymous with both the indoor game and the Three Day Horse Trials Event. What other sport was introduced into Britain there by the 5th Duke of Beaufort?

8 Born at Southam, living and training there, who was the only jockey to win the Grand National five times?

9 Where, on August Bank Holiday Monday, is six-a-side football played in the river Windrush?

10 The smallest twin-engined aircraft in the world operates as part of an AreoSuperbatics (or Crunchy Flying Circus) team. From where?

6 MAINLY ABOUT MUSIC

*The English may not like music,
but they absolutely love the
noise it makes.*

Sir Thomas Beecham (1879-1961)

1 Who became organist at Wyck Rissington church at the age of sixteen, and later composed *The Planet Suite?*

2 Billy Smart's Circus has its permanent winter headquarters in which Cotswold town?

3 Why did Ralph Vaughan Williams name one of his hymn tunes *Down Ampney?*

4 Violet Woodhouse lived at Nether Lypiatt Manor. Of which instruments was she an internationally renowned player?

5 Which musical instruments are made in a Woodchester factory?

6 In which Cotswold church is there an organ which was played by Handel?

7 Who was the Master of Ceremonies who ruled the social scene in Bath for fifty flamboyant years?

8 For what purpose was Cheltenham Music Festival started in 1945?

9 Who was the conductor and what was the famous orchestra most closely associated with it in the early years?

10 On 26 November, 1996, a plaque was erected in Stroud, recording the work there of Joy Batchelor and John Halas. For what are they famous?

7 FAMOUS MEN AND WOMEN

Martyrdom is the only way a man can become famous without ability.

George Bernard Shaw (1856-1950). In Preface to 1908 reprint of *Fabian Essays*.

1 For what great achievement was
   William Tyndale, for a time tutor at Little Sodbury Manor, burnt at
   the stake in the Low Countries in 1536?
2 What was introduced by a relative and namesake of the Reverend
   Rowland Hill of Wootton-under-Edge to gain him a knighthood in
   1861?
3 Who was the astronomer and discoverer of the planet Uranus who
   lived at 19 King Street, Bath?
4 A plaque on a house in Orchard Road, Wootton-under-Edge bears
   the name of the inventor of a 'System . . .known as Phonography in
   the year 1837'. Who was he?
5 And what is phonography?
6 Who was the granddaughter of King Alfred to whom the old
   church at Broadway and the church at Ebrington are dedicated?
7 Who began his career designing furniture for the Lygon Arms at
   Broadway and went on to start a famous furniture design and
   build factory there?
8 Name the international and Olympic horsewoman who lived at
   Miserden and died at her home there in 1996.
9 Who was the Danish inventor of genius who made bicycles in
   Dursley from around 1890?
10 What item of confectionery is associated with Dr William Oliver
   who died at Weston, near Bath in 1764?

8 FLOWERS AND GARDENS

*Show me your garden and I shall tell you
what you are.*

Alfred Austin (1835-1914)

1 As one travels along many Cotswold roads, the hedgerows are covered with *Clematis Vitalba*. What is its common name?

2 Everyone knows that the fields of yellow are oilseed rape, but what are the fields of blue?

3 Who was the poet, satirist and landscape architect who helped Allen Bathurst lay out Cirencester Park?

4 What does Folly Farm, Bourton-on-the-Water, specialise in growing?

5 In which park did Henry Elwes, author of the seven volume work, *The Trees of Great Britain and Ireland,* succeed in establishing the rare Californian nutmeg, Japanese wingnut, Chinese lime and Turkish hazel trees and western red cedars which are among the largest in the country?

6 Name the two famous arboreta in the Cotswolds.

7 And by whom were they founded?

8 According to legend, how many yew trees will only grow at any one time in Painswick churchyard?

9 Two houses – one in the village of Barnsley and the other at Hidcote – have flowers named after them. Name the flowers?

10 Which two local plants were used in the early days of the cloth industry to create dyes?

9 MANY MANSIONS

I know a man that had this trick of melancholy sold a goodly manor for a song.

William Shakespeare. *All's Well That Ends Well.*

1 What is the name of the folly built around 1720 by Lord Bathurst in Cirencester Park?

2 What was the crest of the Tracy family displayed so predominantly on the gatehouse of Stanway House?

3 Charles Wade gave the rooms at Snowshill Manor distinctive names. Name any three of the ten.

4 An upper room at Snowshill Manor (not named by Wade) is known as 'Ann's Room'. Why?

5 Where is Cotswold's newest fort, never used for defence or battle?

6 Where is Worcester Lodge – designed by William Kent and built in 1750 at a cost of £721?

7 When Sir Thomas Phillips died in 1872 he left in his home at Middle Hill, Broadway, the largest private collection of what in the world?

8 Name the house near Avening which has rooms named 'Cromwell' and 'Ireton' after the two Parliamentary generals who stayed there in 1648.

9 The manor house at Cowley was once owned by a member of the family which invented a soothing, malted milk drink. Who was he?

10 This Cotswold house, with a hall dating from the first half of the twelfth century, is considered to be the oldest continually inhabited home in England.

10 AFFAIRS OF STATE

*Government, even in its best state, is
but a necessary evil; in its worst
state, an intolerable one.*

Thomas Paine (1737-1809) in
Common Sense.

1 A Cotswold man, David Hartley, helped to draft the Treaty of
Paris which ended the American War of Independence. Where
was he buried after his death in 1813?

2 The Chartist and champion of popular rights, Feargus O'Connor,
established a Land Settlement project and built five estates of
Charterville cottages and allotments. One was in the Cotswolds
and the well-constructed houses remain today. Where?

3 The last battle between private armies was fought on the
Cotswolds. Where and when?

4 The Chief Baron of the Exchequer to Elizabeth I, the ghost of
whose wife rode across the rooftops of Burford in a chariot of fire
in the eighteenth century bringing misfortune to the townspeople,
is buried in the church of St John the Baptist. His name?

5 What is commemorated by the large archway at Paganhill, Stroud?

6 Sir John Fortescue, who died in 1476, was Lord Chief Justice and
Lord Chancellor to King Henry VI. He was also lord of a Cotswold
manor and has a fine effigy in its church. Where?

7 Which side won the Civil War battle of Stow-on-the-Wold in 1646,
after forcing their opponents' to surrender at Donnington?

8 Who was the British naval officer, owner of a Cotswold estate, who
on 10 November, 1918, with Marshal Foch of France, negotiated
terms of surrender with the German High Command.

9 Blockley was part of Worcestershire for 1,000 years. When was it
transferred to Gloucestershire?

10 Henry I granted borough status to St Edward Stow in 1107. By
what name has the town been known since the sixteenth century?

11 INNS

THE RAM INN

*Come, Come, Come and have a drink
with me
Down at the old Bull and Bush.*

Harry Tilzer (1878-1956).
Song: *Down at the Old Bull and Bush*
sung by Florrie Forde.

1 Where is the Rattlebone Inn and how did it get its name?

2 The inn of which Cotswold village, built in 1777, was referred to by Jane Austen in *Northanger Abbey*?

3 Where is the Mouse Trap public house?

4 A former cloth mill is now a hotel and restaurant and the river Frome passes through waterwheels at either end of the lounge bar. What was the mill called and where is it?

5 Name the pubs at each end of the Sapperton tunnel.

6 What was the original name of the Lygon Arms, Broadway?

7 Where is the Shaven Crown Inn?

8 Where are weary travellers invited to:
> *'Step in and quaff my not brown ale.
> Bright as rubys mild and stale'* for 6d?

9 Where is the Old Corner Cupboard Inn?

10 Where is the Snooty Fox?

12 LITERATURE AND ART

All art deals with the absurd and aims at the simple. Good art speaks truth, indeed is truth, perhaps the only truth.

Iris Murdoch in *The Black Prince.*

1 Who lives near Cirencester and started her rise to stardom in *Opportunity Knocks* on television, reciting her quirky poetry.

2 To which Cotswold town did C R Ashbee move the Guild of Handicrafts from London in 1902?

3 What is the connection betwen the parish of Cowley and *Alice's Adventures in Wonderland*?

4 What is the name of the pub in Slad which, according to Laurie Lee in *Cider with Rosie,* was almost his second home?

5 Which famous author gave Stanway its cricket pavilion and what is his best-loved work?

6 Where did Jane Austen visit her uncle, Theophilus Leigh – a rector here from 1718 to 1762 – and use the Gothic facade of the rectory as a model for *Northanger Abbey*?

7 Her eccentric aristocratic family, on which Nancy Mitford based *Love in a Cold Climate,* lived in a seventeenth century manor house in this village in the Windrush Valley?

8 In 1898, J Arthur Gibbs published *A Cotswold Village.* Which village did it feature?

9 Inscribed on the Mann Institute at Moreton-in-the-Marsh is: *'Every noble life leaves the fibre of it interwoven for ever in the work of the world'*. Who wrote these words?

10 The village of Kelmscot is in part a memorial to this writer and artist who spent the last twenty five years of his life in its Elizabethan manor house.

13 INVENTIONS AND INVENTORS

*Inventions that are not made, like babies that are not born,
are rarely missed.*

J K Galbraith in *The Affluent Society.*

1 Which GWR tunnel, built by Isambard Kingdom Brunel and 3,212 yards long, is so true a piece of engineering that each year, around his birthday on 8 April, the rising sun shines directly through to the western end?

2 Which Cotswold mill was the first to be built of iron and stone throughout so that it was fireproof. And when was it built?

3 Who was the civil engineer, buried in Idbury churchyard, who was responsible for both the original Aswan Dam and the Forth Bridge?

4 The inventions of Joseph Lewis of Brimscombe and Edward Beard Budding of Bisley and Stroud have been of immense help to gardeners. In what way?

5 Who married Catherine Kingscote at St John's church, Kingscote, in 1788, and purchased the Chantry at Avening to begin his married life and to develop his study of vaccination as a preventive treatment for certain diseases?

6 Who was known as 'the father of British geology' and is commemorated by an obelisk at Churchill?

7 Name the Cotswold man who invented the use of negatives in photography?

8 Where can you find a Winchester Standard bushel and peck?

9 Who was the buccaneer, buried at Stanway House in 1742, who invented the medical treatment known as Dover's Powder (10 grains each of opium, ipecacuanha, and sulphate of potash).

10 A Dursley man has a stronger claim to have started the Sunday School movement than Robert Raikes of Gloucester, to whom it is usually attributed. Who was he?

14 MONUMENTS

Can storied urn or animated bust
Back to its mansion call the fleeting breath?
Can honour's voice provoke the silent dust,
Or flatt'ry soothe the dull cold ear of death?

Thomas Gray 1716-1771. *Elegy in a Country Churchyard.*

1　A family whose motto was 'Fortune and Grace', bought the manor of Swinbrook in 1503 but within a century ran out of space in the church for their monuments. So the effigies of six male descendants lie stacked in threes as if in bunk beds, one on top of the other. What is the name of the family?

2　What and where are the Hollings Stones?

3　Memorial brasses in churches are not actually made of brass. What are they made from?

4　What are 'bale' tombs?

5　In the church at Great Barrington there is an effigy of Captain Edmund Bray in Tudor armour, wearing his sword on the right hand side instead of on the left. He was not left handed so why is his sword on the wrong side?

6　Cotswolds' finest assemblage of tombs is in Painswick churchyard, many of them created by John Bryan. What shape did he choose for his own tomb?

7　Which parish church had to be enlarged at the personal expense of Queen Victoria to accommodate a monument she ordered removed from St George's Chapel, Windsor?

8　Where is the only example in England of an out-of-doors 'Poor Souls' Light'?

9　In which church is Thomas the Tank Engine?

10　In which Cotswold church is one of the only two epitaphs in Britain referring to the reign of King Philip and Queen Mary.

15 NATURAL FEATURES

I am a stranger here in Gloucestershire;
These high wild hills and rough, uneven ways
Draw out our miles and make them wearisome.

William Shakespeare, *Richard II*

1 Name the two places that claim to be the source of the River Thames?

2 Eleven rivers flow through the Cotswolds. Name five of them.

3 And which river flows through Upper and Lower Slaughter?

4 What is the acreage of Minchinhampton Common where, in 1743, some 20,000 people gathered to hear Methodist minister, George Whitefield, preach?

5 On which hill, within the ramparts of an Iron Age fort, is the 14ft high, 60ft round natural outcrop known as the Banbury Stone?

6 Which is the larger, the Norfolk Broads or the Cotswold Water Park?

7 Why do the villages of Shipton, Milton and Ascott carry the suffix 'under-Wychwood'?

8 In the history of the manufacture of cloth, one often hears of the 'Stroudwater valleys' How many valleys are there?

9 According to legend, how was Cam Long Down created?

10 The Cotswolds are an AONB, and contain many examples of SSSI What do these initials stand for?

16 COTSWOLD STONE

Has it ever struck you that there's a thin man inside every fat man, just as they say there's a statue inside every block of stone?

George Orwell (1903-1950) in
Coming Up For Air

1 Who was the stone mason from Little Barrington who laid the foundation stone of St Paul' s Cathedral in 1675?

2 From the fifteenth century to the present day stone from Taynton has been used on a number of famous buildings in England. Name three of them.

3 What are 'combers' ?

4 Which church has the largest Cotswold stone porch?

5 Who works with cocks, cussoners, muffety, winetts, becks, batchelors, movedays, nines, wibbuts and cuttings?

6 What is the name given to the large amounts of small pieces of oolitic limestone lying in ploughed fields?

7 What is the order in which brash, clay, weatherstone and rag stone, and freestone are found in a quarry?

8 The boundaries of which counties meet at the Three Shires Stone near Marshfield?

9 Cotswold stone varies in colour from district to district, depending on the amount of ferrous oxide in it. From which quarries is it:
(a) golden yellow?
(b) silver grey?
(c) creamy?

10 What is ashlar?

17 ANCIENT HISTORY

*Antiquities are history defaced, or
some remnants of history which
have casually escaped the
shipwreck of time.*

Francis Bacon (1561-1626) in
Advancement of Learning

1 Where can one find the King Stone, the King's Men and the
   Whispering Knights?

2 Belas Knap is a long barrow not far from Winchcombe. What does
   its name mean?

3 The long barrows were made by the Neolithic farmers who lived
   on the hills from around 4000 BC. For what were they used?

4 When did the Belgic Dobunni people set up their tribal capital at
   Bagendon?

5 To which village does the Thor Stone give its name?

6 What was the original name, before the Roman development of the
   town, of the settlement at Cirencester?

7 How many skeletons were discovered in Hetty Pegler's Tump
   when it was excavated in 1854?

8 Which is the largest of the hill forts built by Iron Age people to
   defend their territory by artificially enhancing the naturally steep
   slope of the Cotswold scarp?

9 How many such hill forts have been identified on the Cotswolds?

10 The Whitlestone, which reputedly goes to drink in the Dikler river,
   is preserved in the paddock of the vicarage in which village?

18 ROYALTY

What I say dose it matter we cant all be of the Blood royal can we.

Daisy Ashford (1881-1972) in *The Young Visiters*

1 Which town was the seat of Mercian royalty, and capital of the sub-kingdom of the Hwicce?

2 Edgar, first king of all England, was crowned in AD 973. Where?

3 And who was the king crowned with his mother's bracelet at the age of nine in Gloucester cathedral?

4 Which former queen of England is buried at Sudeley castle?

5 Which king arrested Sudeley Castle's owner, Ralph Boteler, for treason in order to acquire the site for himself.

6 A basement garden in Laura Place, Bath, contains Mad Eli's collection of gnomes, and what else?

7 How did Charles II and 'witty Pretty Nell' (Gwyn) display their fondness for Burford?

8 Where is the state bed prepared by William Blathwayt for Queen Anne should she ever visit his house. She never did?

9 Which king, in gratitude for their help in aiding his escape, sent Mrs Huntley, the wife of the owner of Boxwell Court, from his exile in France, a turquoise ring which is still in the family's possession?

10 What is the Boleyn Cup and where is it kept?

19 ROMAN REMAINS

Today the Roman and his trouble
Are ashes under the Uricon.

A E Housman (1859-1936) in *The Welsh Marches.*

1 *Felix domesticus* was brought here by the Romans. What is it?

2 What is a hypocaust?

3 What creature forms the centrepiece of the modern version of a Roman mosaic floor displayed in Cirencester's Brewery Centre?

4 The mosaic floor of the west wing of Chedworth's Roman villa is on display at the award winning Corinium Museum, Cirencester. What does it depict ?

5 Which god was worshipped at the altar in the villa at Chedworth?

6 Who was the Celtic/Roman deity, goddess of wisdom and healing, of the temple at Bath?

7 The Romans introduced the European edible snail and three different types of fruit trees that can be found in English orchards. Name one.

8 Where, in 1793, did Samuel Lysons discover a magnificent Roman villa with a tesselated pavement showing Orpheus charming the animals with his music?

9 Britain's first military frontier road was what we know as the Fosse Way (A429). It runs through the Cotswolds, but where in England did it start and where did it finish?

10 Around AD 300 the Romans divided Britain into four provinces. What name was given to the province of which Corinium (Cirencester) became the capital.

20 SAINTS AND SINNERS

We love the windows bright
With red and yellow paints
Presenting to our sight
The better class of Saints

Mgr Ronald Knox (1888-1957). Hymn parody.

1 Where is the only complete set of medieval stained glass windows to survive in the whole of the British Isles?

2 Their design is attributed to Henry VII's Master Glass Painter. What was his name?

3 '. . . the Blood of Christ that is in Hailes' wrote Geoffrey Chaucer in *The Pardoner's Tale*. 'At the Blood of Hayles' wrote John Heywood (1497?-1580?). To what were they referring?

4 Who is the Cotswolds' own saint?

5 Where is St Chloe, and why is the district so called?

6 Where, in the Cotswolds, did the visionary Joanna Southcott live; form a cult; and leave her writings in a 'great box'?

7 On 14 July 1833 at St Mary's Oxford, a former curate of Southrop and Eastleach preached a sermon which led to the foundation of the Oxford Movement. Who was he?

8 What was the name of the vicar of Holy Rood, Ampney Crucis, whose parishioners petitioned Parliament in December, 1640, to have him removed, claiming he was a 'scandalous, persecuting, quarrelsome, bold, uncivill and ignorant Minister'?

9 In which churchyard is the last Englishman to be hanged for highway robbery buried?

10 Which wood is reputedly haunted by the ghost of George Melling, the last shepherd to be hanged in England for sheep stealing?

21 TRANSPORT

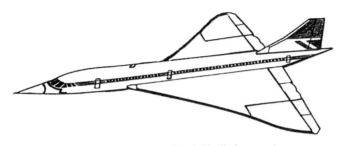

Does the road wind uphill all the way?
Yes, to the very end.
Will the day's journey take the whole long day
From morn to night, my friend.
Christina Rossetti (1830-1894) *Up-Hill.*

1 When and where was the first successful British Concorde test flight?

2 Where can you 'Steam along on a Santa Special'?

3 Where, and from what, was the first successful parachute jump by an Englishman made?

4 Which tunnel, completed in 1789, has a triumphal arch for the deities Isis and Sabrina at its eastern end?

5 Why at Duntisbourne Leer and Chipping Campden is water channelled into the road?

6 What is significant about the design of the lengthsmen's houses built in the 1780s on the Thames and Severn canal?

7 Where is the oldest fingerpost on the Cotswolds, and probably in Britain?

8 What was the saltway, which crosses the Cotswolds to Lechlade?

9 'All roads lead to Stow' was an old saying. How many roads meet here?

10 Where did it cost 3d for 'every Horse or other Beast drawing any Coach', 1d for ' every horse, Mule, Ass laden but not drawing', and 3d for every ' drove of Oxen, Cows or other meat cattle' ?

22 CHURCHES

The Church's Restoration
In eighteen eighty three
Has left for contemplation
Not what there used to be.
John Betjeman(1906-1984) Hymn.

1 Where is the only Cotswold church with a dome?

2 In 1800 the stained glass from the east window of which church was moved 'on loan' to St John the Baptist, Cirencester, and despite many promises has never been returned?

3 On what date is the annual 'Clypping' ceremony at Painswick?

4 What form does it take and how is each child taking part rewarded?

5 In which church can you see the results of a Victorian vicar's attempt to recreate the ambience of a medieval church by painting the walls and ceiling?

6 What is the Buckland Maser or Bowl?

7 Where is the smallest church on the Cotswolds?

8 What are carved on the fifteenth century tower of St James church, Cranham, to denote that it was financed by wool merchants?

9 In which church can you find an early medieval inscription granting indulgence from 1,000 days in Purgatory?

10 As the result of a dream what did the vicar construct beside St Laurence's church, Wyck Rissington in 1952?

23 VILLAGES AND TOWNS

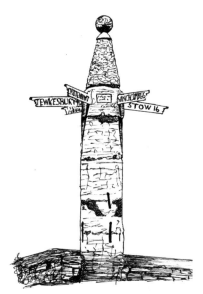

Stow on the Wold
Where the wind blows cold.
Local rhyme

1 Supply the word missing from the second line the old epithet:

   'Mincing Hampton and Painswick Proud,
   *   Beggarley Bisley and . . . . Stroud'*

2 How many Duntisbournes are there in the Cotswolds?

3 In which village are the streets of Upper-up and Bow-wow?

4 Where is the annual 'Pigface Sunday' festival held?

5 New Orleans is famous for its ironlace house decoration and balconies, but one Cotswold town has more wrought iron balconies than anywhere else in the world. Which town?

6 How many bridges cross the river Windrush at Bourton-on-the-water?

7 To what, which or whom is the Bledisloe Cup awarded annually?

8 For which industry did Blockley become famous in the nineteenth century?

9 From which village did Henry Ford buy the blacksmith's forge and a seventeenth century cottage, take them down stone by stone and rebuild them in the Ford Museum at Dearborn, USA?

10 What is manufactured at Postlip Mill?

24 WOOL AND CLOTH

Baa, baa, black sheep
Have you any wool?
Yes sir, yes sir,
Three bags full:
Nursery rhyme

1 What was special about the Cotswold Lion sheep and their fleece?

2 Where can you still see weavers making cloth in the traditional way?

3 Before the advent of camouflage clothing for soldiers, blue and scarlet woollens were a conspicuous part of their uniform. Where were these cloths made?

4 What is the name given to the layer of clay which lies between Great and Inferior Oolite in certain areas of the Cotswolds, and was an essential ingredient in cleaning cloth?

5 Before becoming a terrace of private houses and owned by the National Trust, what was Arlington Row at Bibury?

6 For the storage of what involved with the production of cloth was the round building on the Stroud to Nailsworth road (A46) at South Woodchester, built?

7 And for what process in the production of cloth were the stored items used?

8 Many of Chalford's streets are too steep and narrow for carts or wagons, yet large amounts of material for the cloth trade were moved about here. How?

9 In Tetbury on Spring Bank Holiday Monday, the annual World Championships are raced between relay teams of four runners up and down the 1 in 4 gradient of Gumstool Hill. What do the runners carry?

10 Why is the valley of the river Frome called the Golden Valley?

25 THE ODD AND THE UNUSUAL

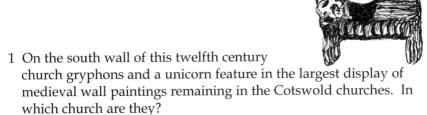

The statue, tolerant through years of weather
Spares the untidy Sunday throng its look.
John Berryman (1914-1972) *The Statue.*

1 On the south wall of this twelfth century
   church gryphons and a unicorn feature in the largest display of
   medieval wall paintings remaining in the Cotswold churches. In
   which church are they?

2 What are known locally as the Winchcombe Worthies?

3 What is thought to be the oldest piece of wood carving in the
   country is in the church of All Hallows in South Cerney. What
   form does it take?

4 Pie Powder Court or *Curia Pedis Pulverizati* was set up in Market
   Street, Wootton-under-Edge in the sixteenth century. For what
   purpose?

5 There is a manticore carved on the south wall of the church at
   North Cerney. What is a manticore?

6 In which Cotswold church can one find wooden mice, the
   'signature' of the craftsman Robert Thomson of Kilburn, Yorkshire,
   carved on the doors, desk, pulpit and pews?

7 What is a Sheila-na-gig, and where can one be seen?

8 What are the small, crude crosses often found inscribed on
   Cotswold church porches or outside walls?

9 The horse shoe on the door of Kempsford church was cast when
   a fourteenth century nobleman was riding to the rescue of his son
   who was drowning in the river nearby? Who was the horseman?

10 What was the purpose of the sun dials scratched on the exterior
    walls of many pre-Reformation churches in the Cotswolds and
    elsewhere?

26 FOOD AND DRINK

It was my Uncle George who discovered alcohol was a food well in advance of medical thought.

P G Wodehouse in *The Luck of the Bodkins*

1 Where, in the Cotswolds in 1846, was the first agricultural college in England founded?

2 A sixteenth century cloth mill, which had been in the possession of the same family since 1827, was converted to a brewery in 1865. Name the family who owned it?

3 And what is the name of the brewery?

4 Only one dairy farm in Gloucestershire makes yoghurt. Where is it?

5 What is a skep?

6 What was the basis of mead, the medieval alcoholic drink made in the abbeys on the Cotswolds?

7 Who, and where, is the only cheesemaker still making Double and Single Gloucester in the traditional manner?

8 For what food-orientated venture is the Dikler river at Donnington known?

9 Where in the Cotswolds are seven varieties of vine grown for wine?

10 In 1758 the Reverend Edward Stone of Chipping Norton chewed a twig of white willow to ease pain and fever, an old folk remedy. He was so impressed with its effects that in 1763 he wrote to the Royal Society describing its benefits. Of which drug was this the basis?

27 IN MEMORIAM

' *God grant that I may fish until my dying day*
And when it comes to my last cast
I humbly pray
When in the Lord's safe landing net
I'm peacefully asleep
I be judged good enough to keep'

1 Of which fishing man is the above poem a memorial, and where is it?

2 Name two of the wool merchants or mercers who have memorial brasses in Northleach church?

3 Where is this epitaph to Samuel Horrell, shepherd, who died in 1807:

> *'From youth through life the sheep was his care*
> *And harmless as his flock his manners were*
> *On earth he held the faith to Christians given*
> *In hope to join the fold of Christ in heaven'*

4 Where can you see an inscribed wooden memorial plaque to a trout?

5 Where is buried 'Puff, the bravest cat in the world, beloved by all', who died in 1996?

6 What is engraved on Giles Hancox's memorial brass in Holy Rood church, Daglingworth?

7 What was the trade of Phillis Humphreys who died in June, 1763, and is buried in Chipping Norton churchyard?

8 Where is the memorial to Sir Bevil Grenville, who was killed in a Civil War battle on 5 July, 1643?

9 Who was the 'flying monk' depicted in a stained glass window in Malmsbury Abbey?

10 What was erected in 1846, and where, to the memory of General Lord Robert Edward Henry Somerset who was commended by Parliament for his drive and enthusiasm at the Battle of Waterloo?

28 A MISCELLANY

Waste not your Hour, or in the vain pursuit
Of This and That endeavour and dispute.

Edward Fitzgerald (1809-1883)
The Rubaiyat of Omar Khayyam

1 Which famous car club has its headquarters at Prescott Speed Hill Climb Circuit, at Prescott, Gotherington?

2 Where annually in July is held an International Brick Throwing and a Rolling Pin Throwing contest, for men and women respectively?

3 Leslie Gillett, whose home is at Blockley, is a World Champion at which sport?

4 In the late 1920s, a Chipping Campden man, already famous for collecting shrubs and plants, was appointed director of the Arnold Arboretum at Harvard University; he also has a memorial garden dedicated to him in his home town. Who was he?

5 How long is the Cotswold Way?

6 Which Cotswold pub claims to be the most haunted in England?

7 The trackbed of which old railway runs through Cotswold Water Park?

8 Where is displayed the largest kettle on the Cotswolds?

9 The diaries of Reverend Francis Edward Witts have recently been published as *The Diary of a Cotswold Parson*. Of which parish was he rector?

10 In which Cotswold town is there a museum of costume and jewellery?

29 PICTURE QUIZ
TOWNS

29 PICTURE QUIZ – TOWNS

1 Where can these armless Grecian graces post letters?

2 Who were the original residents of these almshouses?

29 PICTURE QUIZ – TOWNS

3 No longer used as a cloth mill, what is it now?

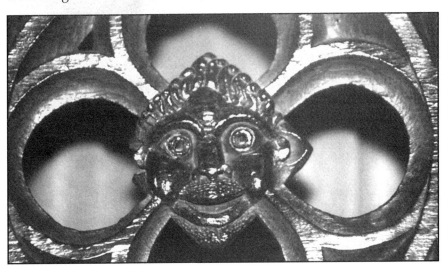

4 Where, if you look carefully, can you find this cheeky chappy?

5 What kind of business goes on in the premises beneath this sign?

6 What makes this post office at Painswick so special?

7 This gateway has two unusual open finials. Why?

8 What fight ended here?

30 PICTURE QUIZ – COUNTRY

9 In what other ways is this Stow-in-the-Wold antiques shop curious?

10 Where is this
   museum cum
   flower stall?

1 This cross is a clue to the name of the village in the churchyard of which it stands.

2 In the grounds of which eighteenth century house is this orangery?

3 In which churchyard is this group of tombs?

4 What is symbolised by the nails carved on this roof boss in Cranham church?

30 PICTURE QUIZ – COUNTRY

5 This is not a house porch. What is it?

6 Where is this powerful sculpture?

7 What is this former hermit's cell made from?

8 Although this pub at Quenington is now closed, what was its former claim to fame?

9 Why did mothers push babies through the hole in this stone?

10 In which church is this three-decker pulpit?

ANSWERS

1 COUNTY RECORDS

1 The Tyndale tower at North Nibley, commemorating William Tyndale who may have been born nearby, is 111 feet high.
2 When Broadway Tower was built in 1799 by the Earl of Coventry as a present for his wife, thirteen counties could be seen from it.
3 Surrounding Cirencester Park, home of Lord Apsley.
4 Badminton, seat of the Duke of Beaufort.
5 The village pub at Barnsley is called 'Village Pub'.
6 Stow-on-the-Wold, at 800ft above sea level.
7 On West Down at the southern point of Cleeve Common.
8 It is 1,083 feet above sea level.
9 The Wishing Clock, Cheltenham.
10 At Winchcombe.

2 ALL ABOUT ANIMALS

1 Trout farming.
2 Off the High Street, in an alley running alongside Woolworth's.
3 Highland cattle.
4 In a field opposite the main entrance is a dovecote built above an open pen for cattle.
5 'Cubs' were pens for holding sheep for market and cost 1s per score.
6 Len Hill, who filled the grounds of Chardwar Manor with sixty different species of birds from all over the world.
7 Penguins.
8 The greyhound in Shakespeare's *Merry Wives of Windsor*, a reference to Dover's Games when a silver collar was awarded to the best dog at coursing.
9 Old Smelly.
10 Under an obelisk in the grounds of Nether Lypiatt Manor.

3 BIRDS – AND SOME BEASTS

1 He is the pelican mascot of RAF Red Arrows aerobatic flying team and lives at Birdland, Bourton-on-the-Water.

2 Stow Horse Fair.

3 At the Cotswold Wildlife Park, Burford.

4 Brockhampton.

5 In the grounds of Lower Slaughter Manor House (now an hotel).

6 The revolving ladder from which can be reached all the nesting boxes inside a dovecote.

7 A loft in which the vicar kept pigeons to supplement his income and his diet.

8 Squabs.

9 A homing pigeon.

10 The Wildfowl and Wetland Trust at Slimbridge.

4 CRIME AND PUNISHMENT

1 Cirencester, Filkins, Bisley, Bibury.

2 The unusual twin-celled lockup at Cirencester, now in the Council Offices car park.

3 Seven.

4 Behind the churchyard at Painswick is a set of iron stocks shaped like a pair of spectacles, last used in 1840, and the only ones of this design in Britain.

5 The alleged murder of William Harrison in 1660 for which Joan Perry and her two sons, Richard and John, were hanged only for Harrison to return to Chipping Camden two years later with a strange story, which could not be substantiated, of being robbed, kidnapped and held in slavery.

6 Tom and Harry Dunsdon.

7 The Earl and Countess of Somerset. Both were sentenced to hang but released on the orders of the King James after a short time in prison – causing public accusations of corruption.

8 Sir George Onesipherus Paul.

9 Gloucester, Horsley, Littledean.

10 The poachers were tried, found guilty and hanged for the murder of gamekeeper John Millins. Later a dying man in nearby Leafield confessed to killing Millins accidentally, thinking he was a deer.

5 SPORTS AND PASTIMES

1 Cheeses weighing 7lbs (3.17kg). Anyone catching a cheese keeps it.

2 Chipping Norton.

3 Salisbury racecourse.

4 Originally they were held on Cleeve Common, but they are now held at Prestbury Park racecourse.

5 Murphy's Gold Cup, as part of the three day Murphy's Irish Craic meeting.

6 Queen Mother Champion Chase.

7 Fox hunting, after a disappointing pursuit of deer in the 1760s.

8 George Stevens, in 1856, 1863, 1864, 1869, and 1870.

9 Bourton-on-the-Water.

10 The 13 feet long, 180 lbs twin engined aircraft takes off from the roof of a Mitsubishi VC Shogun at the former World War One Royal Flying Corps airfield at Rendcomb.

6 MAINLY ABOUT MUSIC

1 Gustav Holst.

2 Chipping Norton.

3 He was born at Down Ampney, where his father was vicar, in 1872.

4 Clavichord and harpsichord.

5 Pianos.

6 St Mary the Virgin, Wotton-under-Edge. The organ was given to St Martin's-in-the-Fields by George I in 1726 at a cost of £1,600 and there it was played by Handel. In 1759 it was bought by the Reverend William Tattersall, vicar of Wotton, for £200.

7 Richard (Beau) Nash.

8 To foster contemporary British music.

9 John Barbirolli and the Hallé Orchestra.

10 They are regarded as founders of the British film animation industry in the 1940s. Their best work was the animation of George Orwell's *Animal Farm*, released in 1954.

7 FAMOUS MEN AND WOMEN

1 The first translation of the New Testament into English.

2 The penny post.

3 William Herschel.

4 Sir Isaac Pitman.

5 Shorthand.

6 St Edburga (or Eadburga) abbess of a nunnery founded by Alfred's widow. Her relics are enshrined in Pershore and were the source of many miracles.

7 Sir Gordon Russell.

8 Pat Smythe.

9 Mikael Pedersen. A Dursley Pedersen bicycle was used in 1900 by Harry Green to set up several world records.

10 The Bath Oliver biscuit.

8 FLOWERS AND GARDENS

1 Old Man's Beard or Traveller's Joy.

2 Linseed.

3 Alexander Pope.

4 Lavender.

5 Colesbourne Park.

6 Westonbirt and Batsford.

7 Westonbirt by R S Holford in 1829, Batsford by Baron Redesdale in 1888.

8 Ninety nine.

9 *Lavateria* 'Barnsley', *Lavandula angustifolia* 'Hidcote' and *Hypericum* 'Hidcote' which bears the flowers of any garden hypericum.

10 Dyer's Greenwood or Dyer's Broom (*Genista tinctoria*) used for making a yellow dye, and when mixed with woad or indigo could produce various shades of green. Dyer's Rocket (*Reseda luteola*) also produced a yellow dye.

9 MANY MANSIONS

1 Alfred's Hall. It bears the date '1085' and is full of dark oak and rusty armour.

2 Scallop shells.

3 The rooms are: Meridian, Mermaid, Admiral, Seraphim, Nadir, Dragon, Top Gallant, Seventh Heaven, Hundred Wheels and Great Garret.

4 In 1604 Ann Parsons was abducted from Elmley Castle to be married secretly at midnight on St Valentine's Eve in this room, 'without benefit of law or Church'.

5 Rodborough Fort, Rodborough Common, is a battlemented house built *c*1870.

6 On the A46, Cirencester to Bath road, near Didmarton. This archetype of the grand gate lodge is at the entrance to Badminton Park, three miles due north of the main house yet in full view of it.

7 Books. It was his declared intention to own a copy of every book in the world.

8 Chavenage.

9 Sir James Horlick, who largely remodelled the house in 1850.

10 Horton Court at Horton. The hall is now all that remains of the house, which is administered by the National Trust.

10   AFFAIRS OF STATE

1 David Hartley was buried at the church of St John the Baptist, Old Sodbury.

2 Minster Lovell.

3 On Nibley Green, North Nibley, on 20 March, 1470, between rival lines of the Berkeley family led respectively by Viscount Lisle and Lord Berkeley.

4 Sir Lawrence Tanfield.

5 William Wilberforce's Emancipation Act of 1833, which effectively ended slavery in the British colonies.

6 The church of St Eadburga at Ebrington.

7 The Parliamentarians.

8 First Sea Lord Admiral Sir Roslyn Wemyss, owner of Stanway House.

9 In 1931, in an adjustment of boundary anomalies.

10 Stow-on-the-Wold.

11 INNS

1 It is at Sherston and is associated with the legend of John Rattlebone, a local man who, with Edmund Ironside, is said to have defeated invading Danes here in 1016.

2 Petty France.

3 Bourton-on-the-Water.

4 It is Egypt Mill at Nailsworth.

5 Daneway and Tunnel House.

6 The White Hart.

7 Shipton-under-Wychwood. It was built as a guesthouse for Bruern Abbey and licensed in 1314.

8 The Plough Inn at Ford has these words on a sign on its outside wall.

9 Winchcombe.

10 Tetbury.

12 LITERATURE AND ART

1 Pam Ayres.

2 Chipping Campden.

3 Charles Lutwidge Dodgson was the rector's nephew and often visited Cowley before he adopted the pseudonym of Lewis Carroll and wrote many of his stories and poems. Another visitor was Alice Liddell, who became the model for *Alice.*

4 The Woolpack.

5 J M Barrie, *Peter Pan.*

6 Adlestrop House, formerly the rectory of St Mary Magdalene church.

7 Asthall.

8 Ablington.

9 John Ruskin.

10 William Morris.

13 INVENTIONS AND INVENTORS

1 Box Tunnel.

2 King's Stanley mill, erected in 1812.

3 Sir Benjamin Baker (1840-1907).

4 In 1815 Joseph Lewis invented the rotary cutter, a rotating drum on which angled blades moved across the surface of cloth and thus replacing cumbersome manual shears used to cut raised nap. Budding, also a cloth worker, applied the principle to cutting grass on lawns, and in 1830 patented the cylinder grass mower.

5 Edward Jenner.

6 George Smith.

7 William Henry Fox Talbot. The world's first photograph – a latticed window – was taken at Lacock Abbey in 1835.

8 In the church of St Laurence, Bourton-on-the-Hill.

9 Thomas Dover – more popularly known as the person who on 2 February, 1709, rescued Alexander Selkirk from Juan Fernandez Island and gave Daniel Defoe the plot of *Robinson Crusoe.*

10 William King.

14 MONUMENTS

1 Fettiplace.

2 Tiers of blocks of stone piled up in Stroud churchyard to mark the burial place of John Hollings, who instructed that he should be buried above ground.

3 Latten, an alloy of copper, zinc, lead and tin.

4 Rounded table tombs, ridged to represent corded bales of wool, and supposedly used only for those merchants who had the right to ship their wool from the fourteen licensed woolstaple towns which regulated the wool export trade.

5 He was pardoned by Elizabeth I for murdering a man in a fit of rage and vowed never to drawn his sword with his right hand again.

6 A pyramid, a miniature version of the tomb of Caius Cestius in Rome.

7 St Michael's church, Great Badminton – to accommodate the huge effigy of the 1st Duke of Beaufort, who had died in 1699.

8 In the churchyard of All Saints, Bisley. Candles were placed in it for masses for the poor.

9 In the 'Awdry Window' of St Mary Magdalene's church at Rodborough.

10 In St Bartholomew's church, Whittington, on a brass with figures of Richard Cotton and his wife, dated 1556.

15 NATURAL FEATURES

1 Thameshead, near Cirencester, and Seven Springs, north of Coberley.

2 Windrush, Eye, Dikler, Churn, Coln, Frome, Leach, Dun, Isbourne, Cam and Evenlode.

3 The River Eye.

4 It covers 580 acres.

5 Bredon Hill.

6 The Cotswold Water Park. It has 132 lakes and is 50 per cent bigger than the Broads.

7 The phrase refers to the position of the villages 'beneath' Wychwood, formerly a royal hunting forest and now a National Nature Reserve.

8 Five.

9 This outlier of the Cotswolds was formed when the Devil, carrying away the hills in barrow loads to dam the Severn, was tricked by a cobbler into tipping his load on to the site.

10 Area of Outstanding Natural Beauty. Site of Special Scientific Interest.

16 COTSWOLD STONE

1 Thomas Strong.

2 Merton College, Oxford, tower (1449); Eton College (1448-57); St George's Chapel, Windsor (1475-83); All Souls and Christ Church Colleges, Oxford (1525-28); St Paul's Cathedral; Blenheim Palace (1704-22); New Bodleian Library, Oxford (1930s).

3 The upright pieces of stone which protect the top of a drystone wall.

4 St John the Baptist, Cirencester.

5 People who make stone roofing slates. They are all names for different sizes of slates.

6 Brash.

7 In that order, from the surface soil to the bottom.

8 Gloucestershire, Wiltshire and Somerset.

9 (a) The quarries above Stanway at Coscombe, (b) the quarries around Painswick and (c) the quarry at Farmington.

10 Large blocks of stone dressed to even faces and squared edges, for building purposes.

17 ANCIENT HISTORY

1 Together they form the Rollright Stones, on the hill above Long Compton.

2 Beacon mound.

3 For the burial of the dead.

4 c500 BC

5 Taston

6 Caer Coryn, *caer* meaning 'fort', *coryn* meaning 'the top part', probably referring to its position on the river Churn.

7 Fifteen.

8 Uleybury at 32 acres, or Salmonsbury Camp.

9 Twenty six.

10 Lower Swell

18 ROYALTY

1 Winchcombe.

2 Bath.

3 Henry III. His coronation was a hasty move, designed to prevent a civil war, and carried out at Gloucester to avoid the delay of a journey to London.

4 Katherine Parr, sixth wife of Henry VIII and the only one to survive him. She came here as the bride of Sir Thomas Seymour but died in childbirth eighteen months later.

5 Edward IV.

6 His collection of royal memorabilia.

7 Their illegitimate son, born in 1670, was created Earl of Burford, and Nell called her rooms at Windsor, Burford House.

8 Dyrham Park.

9 Charles II.

10 This gilt cup surmounted by the badge of Anne Boleyn's family was made for the Henry VIII's young queen and is hallmarked 1535. In 1561 it was given by Elizabeth I to her mother's physician, Dr Richard Masters of Cirencester, and is displayed in Cirencester parish church.

19 ROMAN REMAINS

1 The domestic cat.

2 A system of circulating hot air underneath floors. There is a fine example at Chedworth villa.

3 A hare.

4 The Four Seasons.

5 Mars.

6 Sulis/Minerva.

7 Sweet chestnut, cherry, pear.

8 In the Rowland Hill Tabernacle, Wotton-under-Edge.

9 It is thought to have begun on the Devon coast at the former quarries at Beer, but the first confident marking occurs at Axminster, from where it runs to Lincoln.

10 Britannia Prima.

20 SAINTS AND SINNERS

1 In the church of St Mary, Fairford.

2 Barnard Flower.

3 A holy relic of a phial of fluid, reputedly the Blood of Christ authenticated by the Patriarch of Constantinople, was given to Hailes Abbey in 1270. It was housed in a shrine at the abbey which became an important place of pilgrimage.

4 St Kenelm, whose tomb is at Winchcombe Abbey.

5 St Chloe is a district of Amberley. The name derives from *Sengedleag* – a clearing made by slashing and burning.

6 She lived at Rock Cottage, Blockley, between 1804 and 1814.

7 John Keble.

8 Benedict Grace.

9 Henry Duncan, hanged for highway robbery on 23 February 1822, is buried in the churchyard of St James's, Cranham.

10 Dowdeswell.

21 TRANSPORT

1 In 1969 at RAF Fairford, under the captaincy of Brian Trubshaw.

2 On the GWR (Gloucestershire and Warwickshire Railway) at Toddington.

3 Over Cheltenham's Montpellier Gardens in 1838 by John Hampton from a balloon.

4 The Sapperton Tunnel on the Thames and Severn canal.

5 To wash the wheels of carts and feet of horses.

6 They are round with Gothic window and door details. They have a basement store or stable with living accommodation on two floors above and a roof cistern for catching rain water.

7 At the top of Fish Hill, at the junction of the Moreton-in-Marsh, Broadway and Chipping Campden roads.

8 The system of packhorse routes by which salt was carried from Droitwich across the Cotswolds on its way to Lechlade, for further distribution by river.

9 Eight.

10 At Butter Row Gate, Rodborough, where a list of charges is displayed on the former toll house of 1825.

22 CHURCHES

1 St Lawrence's church at Bourton-on-the-Water.

2 St Peter's, Siddington.

3 On the first Sunday following 19 September.

4 Parishioners and children carrying flowers 'clyp' or encircle the church. The children each receive a bun.

5 At St George's church, Hampnett, and and also at St Mary the Virgin, Lower Swell.

6 A maple wood bowl, formerly used as a loving cup at village weddings.

7 Clapton-on-the-Hill. The nave of St James's church is 30ft by 13ft, the chancel is 15ft by 11ft and there is seating for forty five people.

8 A pair of shears.

9 On the chancel arch of St James's church, Clapton-on-the-Hill.

10 A maze. There is a model of it in the church.

23 VILLAGES AND TOWNS

1 Strutting.

2 Four. Abbots because it was a possession of St Peter's Abbey,

Gloucester; Leer was in the ownership of the Abbey of Lire in Normandy until 1416 when it was given to Cirencester Abbey; Rous was named after the Roux or Rous family, formerly lords of the manor; Middle because that is where it is.

3 South Cerney.

4 Avening.

5 Cheltenham.

6 Four. The narrow bridge erected in 1756, Payne's footbridge of 1776, the road bridge leading to Victoria Road and the road bridge at the end of Sherborne Road.

7 The three best kept villages in Gloucestershire.

8 Silk-throwing.

9 Chedworth. He also shipped over a flock of Cotswold sheep and a dovecote complete with birds.

10 Fine grade and filter paper.

24 WOOL AND CLOTH

1 The Cotswold Lions grew long and thick whitish fleeces with a strong curl and rich lustre. They were noted for their large size and strong necks and their ability to thrive on the herbage from lime rich soil.

2 At the Cotswold Woollen Weavers' Centre, Filkins.

3 Blue at Uley and scarlet at Stroudwater.

4 Fuller's Earth.

5 In the seventeenth century it was converted from a monastic wool barn into a group of weavers' cottages.

6 Teazles.

7 To raise the nap.

8 By pack horse.

9 30kg (65lb) woolsacks.

10 Because of the wealth created by the large number of mills concentrated there. In the 1820s there were 150 working mills in this valley, almost three quarters of the total in the Cotswolds.

25 THE ODD AND THE UNUSUAL

1 Hailes church, opposite the abbey.

2 The forty grotesque heads carved on the parapet of St Peter's church.

3 It is part of a cross.

4 To deal with infringements of the law by travelling traders – those with *pieds poudre* (dusty feet) – at markets and fairs.

5 A mythical creature with the head of a man, body of a lion, a scorpion's sting and porcupine quills.

6 Ilmington.

7 A 'rude' carving of a woman, most likely a pre-Christian fertility symbol or a pagan goddess. There are examples on South Cerney and Oaksey churches.

8 They are votive crosses incised by pilgrims and others setting off on journeys, to seek safe passage.

9 Henry Plantagenet, created first Duke of Lancaster in 1350.

10 They are mass dials, a means by which the clergy, parishioners and passers by could tell the time and attend mass.

26 FOOD AND DRINK

1 Cirencester.

2 The Arkell family.

3 Donnington Brewery.

4 Perrott's Brook, near Cirencester.

5 A basket for keeping bees in, before the development of modern hives.

6 Crushed honeycombs fermented in yeast.

7 Mrs Diana Smart of Smart's Natural Dairy Products, Churcham, Gloucester.

8 Trout farming.

9 At the Windward vineyard, Crickley.

10 Willow bark contains salicylic acid, the basis of aspirin.

27 IN MEMORIAM

1 This memorial is to J R Wingfield and is in St Mary's church, Great Barrington.

2 John Fortey, William Midwinter, Thomas Busshe, John Tayloure, Thomas Fortey, Robert Serche.

3 In St Andrew's churchyard, Miserden.

4 On the wall of Fish Cottage, Blockley.

5 In the garden of the Canal Round House, Chalford.

6 His will – the *Dissecation and Distribution of Giles Hancox*.

7 She was an itinerant rat-catcher.

8 Lansdown Hill, Bath.

9 Elmer or Eilmer, who around AD 1100 made himself wings and attempted to fly from the tower of the abbey. He crash landed and broke both his legs. He later gained fame for having lived long enough to have seen Halley's comet twice.

10 The tall tower at Hawkesbury Upton.

28 A MISCELLANY

1 The Bugatti Owners Club.

2 Stroud.

3 Bowls.

4 Ernest 'Chinese' Wilson.

5 It is 104 miles long. It runs between Lansdown Hill, Bath, and the Market Square, Chipping Campden.

6 The Ram, Wotton-under- Edge.

7 The Swindon and Cricklade Railway.

8 The kettle, which can hold 82 gallons, hangs outside a shop in George Street, Nailsworth.

9 Lower Slaughter.

10 In the Pittville Pump Room at Cheltenham.

29 PICTURE QUIZ – TOWNS

1 In Montpellier, Cheltenham.
2 They are almshouses for six old men and six old women at Chipping Campden.
3 Ebley Mill is now the offices of Stroud District Council.
4 The Winchcombe Imp is on a medieval screen in St Peter's church.
5 It is an estate agent and auctioneer's office.
6 It is the oldest building in Britain used as a post office.
7 The finials serve as chimneys for their respective gatehouses.
8 The last legal duel in England. It was fought at The Grange, Folly Lane, Stroud and 21 year old Lieutenant Joseph Delmont of the 82nd Regiment was killed by Lieutenant Reginald Kemyss.
9 It leans perilously sideways and backwards.
10 The Tolsey is on High Street, Burford.

30 PICTURE QUIZ – COUNTRY

1 The churchyard cross at Ampney Crucis was carved c1415.
2 Barnsley Park. An earlier owner paid a mason £12 to build it.
3 St Michael's churchyard, Winson.
4 The three nails are an emblem of Christ's Passion on the Cross.
5 It is Coln St Aldwyn's village telephone box
6 At Rousham House, overlooking the river Cherwell.
7 It is made from old tree roots and offcuts. It is in Badminton Park.
8 It had the smallest bar in Gloucestershire.
9 They believed that by doing so they would be cured of infantile rickets.
10 St Lawrence's church, Didmarton.

COVER AND TITLE PAGE PICTURES

Front cover: Sezincote
Title page: Carved roadside stones at Guiting Power.
Back cover: The Adderbury Worm on the frieze of St Mary's church, Adderbury.

LINE DRAWINGS ON SPECIFIC SUBJECTS